W9-CTQ-064

Cakewalk In Concert
Song Book

Visit Cakewalk on the World-Wide Web at www.cakewalk.com.

Table of Contents

Key:
◆ Easier   ◆◆ More Difficult

We have specially selected each musical arrangement for use with Cakewalk In Concert to provide you with a wide assortment of styles for beginning and experienced players. The song file for each selection can be found inside In Concert's Music folder, in each publisher's folder.

Cakewalk In Concert also includes a music file for advanced pianists, Mozart's Concerto in D Minor, K. 466: 1st Movement, MIDI orchestration by Frank Weinstock. You will find the song file inside In Concert's Music folder, in the TimeWarp Technologies folder. Several fine print editions of the full score are available at your local music store, or through Music Dispatch. For more information on ordering this concerto see "How to Get More Music" on page 80.

Hal Leonard Student Piano Library

Sampler

Written by
Barbara Kreader • Fred Kern • Phillip Keveren • Mona Rejino

EXCLUSIVELY DISTRIBUTED BY

HAL•LEONARD®
CORPORATION
7777 W. BLUEMOUND RD. P.O. BOX 13819
MILWAUKEE, WISCONSIN 53213

Visit Hal Leonard Online at
www.halleonard.com

Hal Leonard Student Piano Library

A piano method with music to please students, teachers and parents!
The **Hal Leonard Student Piano Library** is clear, concise and carefully graded for the beginning student. Perfect for private and group instruction.

Book 1	
Piano Lessons	00296001
Lessons CD	00296004
Lessons GM Disk	00296005
Piano Practice Games	00296002
Piano Solos	00296003
Solos CD	00296017
Solos GM Disk	00296018
Piano Theory Workbook	00296023

Book 2	
Piano Lessons	00296006
Lessons CD	00296009
Lessons GM Disk	00296010
Piano Practice Games	00296007
Piano Solos	00296008
Solos CD	00296019
Solos GM Disk	00296020
Piano Theory Workbook	00296024

Book 3	
Piano Lessons	00296011
Lessons CD	00296014
Lessons GM Disk	00296015
Piano Practice Games	00296012
Piano Solos	00296013
Solos CD	00296021
Solos GM Disk	00296022
Piano Theory Workbook	00296025

Book 4	
Piano Lessons	00296026
Lessons CD	00296029
Lessons GM Disk	00296030
Piano Practice Games	00296027
Piano Solos	00296028
Solos CD	00296036
Solos GM Disk	00296037
Piano Theory Workbook	00296038

Piano Practice Games
Theory, technique and creativity correlated with music in the lesson book

Piano Solos
Performance repertoire correlated with concepts in the lesson book

Piano Theory Workbook
Writing activities to review theory introduced in the lesson book

Piano Lessons
New concepts introduced with appealing music

Instrumental Accompaniments
Audio CD or General MIDI disk correlated with music in the lesson and games book

Instrumental Accompaniments
Audio CD or General MIDI disk correlated with music in the solo book

Hal Leonard Student Piano Library

Piano Lessons Book 2

FLAT

♭

A **Flat** sign before a note means to play the next key to the left, either black or white.

A Little Latin

Moderately fast

Bill Boyd

mp

Accompaniment (Student plays one octave higher than written.)

Moderately fast (♩=170)

Hal Leonard Student Piano Library

Piano Lessons Book 2

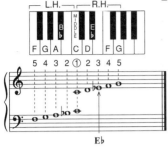

ACCENT

>

An **Accent** over or under a note means to play that note louder.

Stompin'

Keep the beat! (♩=190)

Bill Boyd

D♯ is the same piano key as E♭.

Hal Leonard Student Piano Library

Piano Lessons Book 3

Lavender Mood

Sweetly

Folk Tune

Accompaniment (Student plays two octaves higher than written.)

Sweetly (♩=102)

With pedal

Baroque Boogie

for Sean David

Boogie! (swing eighth notes)

Phillip Keveren

Hal Leonard Student Piano Library

Piano Solos Book 3

The Winter Wind

Swirling fast

Carol Klose

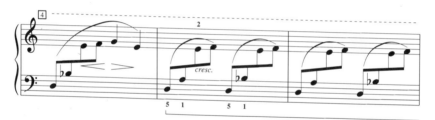

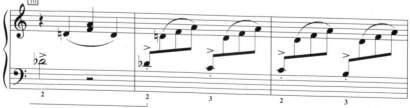

Hal Leonard Student Piano Library

Piano Lessons Book 4

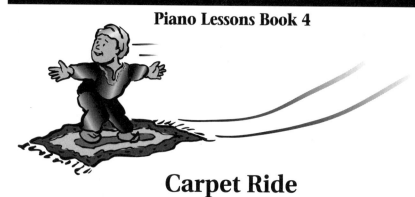

Carpet Ride

Joshua Fit The Battle Of Jericho

Theme and Variations

CHANGING METERS

This piece uses a different time signature for the theme and each variation:

$\frac{4}{4}$ for the Traditional style,

$\frac{3}{4}$ for the Classical style, and

$\frac{4}{4}$ for the Jazz style.

Theme: **Traditional**
Allegretto (♩=170)

Phillip Keveren

Variation I: **Classical**
Fleeting (♩=185) *1st time both hands 8va*

Clap and count these patterns:

Doo Wop Ditty

Happily, in no big hurry (♩=65)

Phillip Keveren

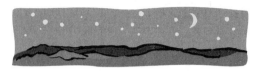

FINGER SUBSTITUTION

Sometimes a phrase extends beyond the range of a five-finger pattern. To keep the sound smooth and connected, substitute one finger for another on the repeated note.

Starry Night

Andante (♩=98)

Italo Taranta

Longing

Andante con moto (♩.=35)

Barbara Kreader

Hal Leonard Student Piano Library

Piano Lessons Book 4

Allegro

from *Eine Kleine Nachtmusik*

Wolfgang A. Mozart
(1756-1791)
Adapted by Fred Kern

Outstanding Piano Collections
with Accompanying General MIDI Disks

Cakewalk *In Concert* features selections from the following collections:

● A Merry Little Christmas

7 New Arrangements of Christmas
Favorites for Late Elementary to
Early Intermediate Pianists
by Kenon D. Renfrow

(16883) $4.95

● Romantic Impressions

Solos in the Romantic Style that
Develop Expressive Playing
by Martha Mier

(6688) $5.95, Book 1: Early Intermediate to Intermediate
(6689) $5.95, Book 2: Intermediate to Late Intermediate

● Jazz, Rags & Blues

Original Fun-Filled Pieces that Reflect
the Various Styles of Jazz
by Martha Mier

(6642) $5.50, Book 1: Late Elementary to Early Intermediate
(6643) $5.50, Book 2: Early Intermediate to Intermediate

● Jazz SophistiCAT

Sophisticated and Motivational
Jazz Solos for Pianists
by Dennis Alexander & Dennis Thurmond

(14715) $4.95, Solo Book 1: Late Elementary to Early Intermediate
(14716) $4.95, Solo Book 2: Intermediate

● First Favorite Classics

Favorite Pieces for Students from the Four
Stylistic Periods of Piano Repertoire
*Selected & Edited by E. L. Lancaster &
Kenon D. Renfrow.*

(14713) $5.95, Solo Book 1: Elementary to Late Elementary
(16810) $7.95, Solo Book 2: Late Elementary to Early Intermediate

● Just for You

A Collection of Pieces in a Wide Variety
of Styles and Moods. Specially Written
to Inspire, Motivate and Entertain
by Dennis Alexander

(405) $5.95, Book 1: Elementary
(406) $5.95, Book 2: Late Elementary to Early Intermediate
(407) $5.95, Book 3: Early Intermediate to Intermediate

● Favorite Classics

Favorite Pieces for Students from the Four
Stylistic Periods of Piano Repertoire
*Selected & Edited by E. L. Lancaster &
Kenon D. Renfrow.*

(6023) $7.50, Book 1: Early Intermediate to Late Intermediate

● Hanon
The Virtuoso
Pianist in
60 Exercises

Edited by Allan Small

(616) $6.95

GENERAL MIDI

FREE DISK!

**Order 3 disks from Alfred and
receive a 4th disk FREE.**
(up to a $9.95 value)

*Please choose your titles from
the list on the following page.*

See the following page for a complete listing of Alfred's General MIDI disks, including disks for our best-selling piano method.

General MIDI
Alfred's Basic Piano Library Prep Course

Disks for Lesson Books
Level A	$14.95	5700 _____
Level B	$14.95	5717 _____
Level C	$14.95	5718 _____
Level D	$14.95	5719 _____
Level E	$14.95	5720 _____
Level F	$14.95	5721 _____

Disks for Solo Books
Level A	$14.95	14415 _____
Level B	$14.95	14416 _____
Level C	$14.95	14417 _____
Level D	$14.95	14418 _____
Level E	$14.95	14419 _____
Level F	$14.95	14420 _____

Alfred's Basic Piano Library

Disks for Lesson Books
Level 1A	$14.95	8589 _____
Level 1B	$14.95	8583 _____
Level 2	$14.95	8569 _____
Level 3	$14.95	8561 _____
Level 4	$14.95	8556 _____

Disks for Recital Books
Level 1A	$14.95	8588 _____
Level 1B	$14.95	8581 _____
Level 2	$14.95	8567 _____
Level 3	$14.95	8558 _____
Level 4	$14.95	8549 _____

Disks for Technic Books
Level 1A	$14.95	8523 _____
Level 1B	$14.95	8536 _____
Level 2	$14.95	8538 _____
Level 3	$14.95	8539 _____

Disks for All-in-One Course
Level 1	$14.95	14410 _____
Level 2	$14.95	14411 _____
Level 3	$14.95	14412 _____
Level 4	$14.95	14413 _____
Level 5	$14.95	14414 _____

Disks for Fun Books
Level 1A	$14.95	8590 _____
Level 1B	$14.95	8586 _____
Level 2	$14.95	8571 _____
Level 3	$14.95	8565 _____

Disks for Hymn Books
Level 1A	$14.95	8515 _____
Level 1B	$14.95	8587 _____
Level 2	$14.95	8576 _____
Level 3	$14.95	8566 _____

Disks for Ear Training
Level 1A	$14.95	14446 _____
Level 1B	$14.95	14447 _____
Level 2	$14.95	14448 _____
Level 3	$14.95	14449 _____
Level 4	$14.95	14450 _____

Disks for Ensemble Books
Levels 1A–3	$14.95	8597 _____

Disks for Merry Christmas!
Levels 1A–2	$14.95	5722 _____

Disks for Christmas Ensembles
Levels 1A–1B	$14.95	5716 _____
Levels 2–3	$14.95	14434 _____

Disks for Jazz/Rock Course and Performance Books
Level 1	$14.95	5726 _____
Level 2	$14.95	5727 _____
Level 3	$14.95	5728 _____
Level 4	$14.95	5729 _____

Alfred's Basic Adult Piano Course

Disk for Lesson Book
Level 1	$14.95	8490 _____
Level 2	$14.95	14429 _____

Disks for All-in-One Course
Book 1	$14.95	5725 _____
Book 2	$14.95	14428 _____

Alfred's Group Piano for Adults
Book 1 (16 disks)	$125.00	14029 _____
Book 2 (15 disks)	$125.00	14752 _____

Alfred's Masterwork Series

Disks for Bach/Inventions and Sinfonias
Performance only	$14.95	5714 _____

Disks for Hanon/Book 1
w/Background Accompaniments	$14.95	5715 _____

Other General MIDI Disks from Alfred

Alfred's Basic Group Piano Course
General MIDI Disk—Book 1	$14.95	18086 _____
General MIDI Disk—Book 2	$14.95	18088 _____
General MIDI Disk—Book 3	$14.95	18091 _____
General MIDI Disk—Book 4	$14.95	18094 _____

Christmas Tree-O!, A (Alexander)
General MIDI Disk	$9.95	14516 _____

City Scenes (Miller)
Book and General MIDI Disk	$14.95	11751 _____
General MIDI Disk only	$8.00	5723 _____

Concertino in D Major (Alexander)
General MIDI Disk	$9.95	14669 _____

Favorite Classics
General MIDI Disk—Book 1	$9.95	14425 _____

First Favorite Classics
General MIDI Disk—Book 1	$9.95	17250 _____
General MIDI Disk—Book 2	$9.95	17251 _____

Jazz, Rags, and Blues (Mier)
General MIDI Disk—Book 1	$9.95	14423 _____
General MIDI Disk—Book 2	$9.95	14424 _____
General MIDI Disk—Book 3 (available summer 1998)	$9.95	18123 _____

Jazz SophistiCat Series, The (Alexander/Thurmond)
General MIDI Disk—Solo Book 1	$9.95	14406 _____
General MIDI Disk—Solo Book 2	$9.95	14407 _____
General MIDI Disk—Duet Book 1	$9.95	14408 _____
General MIDI Disk—Duet Book 2	$9.95	14409 _____

Just for You (Alexander)
General MIDI Disk—Book 1	$9.95	14437 _____
General MIDI Disk—Book 2	$9.95	14438 _____
General MIDI Disk—Book 3	$9.95	14439 _____

Merry Little Christmas, A (Renfrow)
General MIDI Disk	$9.95	14442 _____

Music Thru MIDI (Alexander/Gordon/Thurmond)
General MIDI Disk	$14.95	8429 _____

Romantic Impressions (Mier)
General MIDI Disk—Book 1	$9.95	14421 _____
General MIDI Disk—Book 2	$9.95	14422 _____
General MIDI Disk—Book 3 (available summer 1998)	$9.95	18122 _____

Time Traveler's Guide to Music History (Christiansen/Mitchell)
General MIDI Disk—Book 1	$9.95	14527 _____
General MIDI Disk—Book 2	$9.95	14528 _____

Please choose your titles from the list above

HOW TO ORDER:

By Phone: Call 818-892-2452 today and order your General MIDI disks using your Visa or Mastercard.

By Mail: Write request on a separate sheet or photocopy this order form and include the following information—name, address, phone, MIDI titles, check or credit card no. with expiration date. Please include $3 for shipping.

(CA, FL, MN, NY, PA, SC, TX, WA residents add applicable sales tax.)   Offer #81820

Mail to: Alfred Publishing Co., Inc.
P.O. Box 10003
Van Nuys, CA 91410-0003

818-891-5999

Jolly Old Saint Nicholas

Traditional
Arr. by Kenon D. Renfrow

Selections from Alfred Publishing • Jolly Old Saint Nicholas

Selections from Alfred Publishing • Jolly Old Saint Nicholas

Clarinet Blues

Soulfully, with slow blues swing (♪♪ = ♩³♪)
(♩ = 88)

Martha Mier

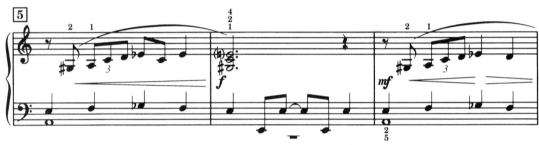

"Clarinet Blues" from JAZZ, RAGS & BLUES, Book 2, by Martha Mier
Copyright © MCMXCIII by Alfred Publishing Co., Inc.

Selections from Alfred Publishing • Clarinet Blues

SPOOKS FROM MARS

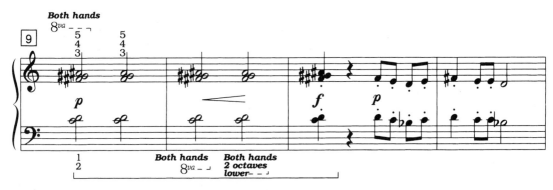

"Spooks from Mars" from JUST FOR YOU, Book 1, by Dennis Alexander
Copyright © MCMLXXXIX by Alfred Publishing Co., Inc.

Selections from Alfred Publishing • Spooks from Mars

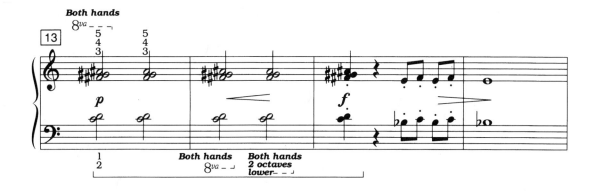

BRIGHT RED!

"Bright Red!" from JUST FOR YOU, Book 2, by Dennis Alexander
Copyright © MCMLXXXIX by Alfred Publishing Co., Inc.

Selections from Alfred Publishing • Bright Red

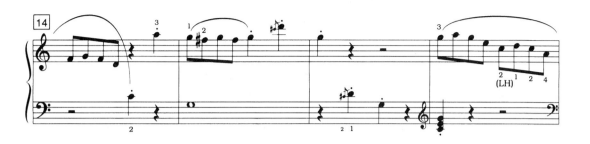

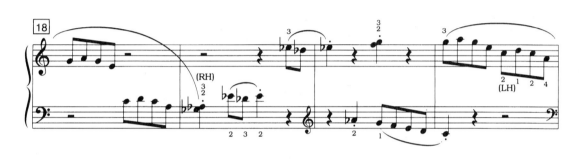

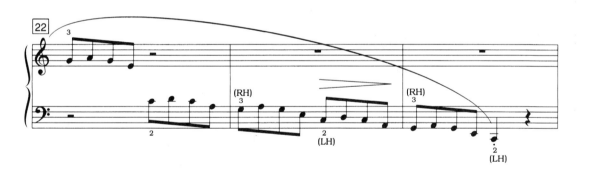

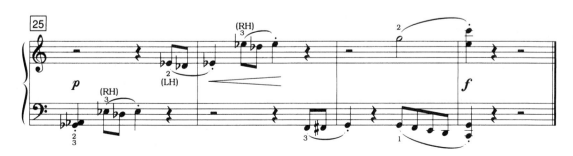

Selections from Alfred Publishing • Bright Red

RAGGEDY RAG

"Raggedy Rag" from JUST FOR YOU, Book 3, by Dennis Alexander
Copyright © MCMLXXXIX by Alfred Publishing Co., Inc.

NOCTURNE IN E♭

"Nocturne in E♭" from JUST FOR YOU, Book 3, by Dennis Alexander
Copyright © MCMLXXXIX by Alfred Publishing Co., Inc.

Selections from Alfred Publishing • Noctune in E♭

Boogie to the Right

Dennis Thurmond
Dennis Alexander

"Boogie to the Right" from JAZZ SOPHISTICAT, Solo Book 1, by Dennis Alexander and Dennis Thurmond
Copyright © MCMXCV by Alfred Publishing Co., Inc.

36

Folk Dance
(The First Term at the Piano)

🔊 9 (32)

Béla Bartók
(1881–1945)

Selections from Alfred Publishing • Folk Dance

Etude

Fanfare

🔊 **22 (45)**

William Duncombe
(18th century)

Minuet in F Major

21 (54)

Wolfgang Amadeus Mozart
(1756–1791)
K. 2

Allegretto

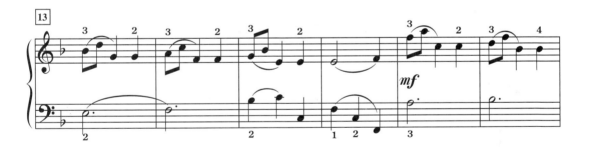

The Wild Rider
Op. 68, No. 8

Robert Schumann
(1810-1856)

"Wild Rider" from FAVORITE CLASSICS, Solo Book 1,
selected and edited by E. L. Lancaster and Kenon D. Renfrow
Copyright © MCMXCI by Alfred Publishing Co., Inc.

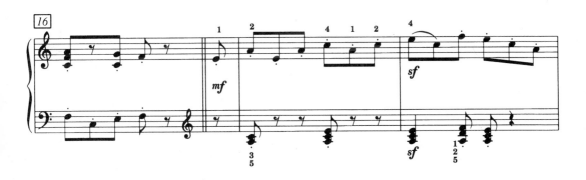

THE VIRTUOSO PIANIST, PART 1

Preparatory Exercises to Acquire Speed, Precision, Agility and Strength in the Fingers of Both Hands as well as Flexibility of the Wrists.

The two "Metronome Marks" (M.M.) at the head of the first exercise means to begin playing at "60" and gradually increase the speed to "108". Play all exercises in Part 1 in this manner.

Exercise 1 gives practice in stretching the 4th and 5th fingers of the left hand while ascending, the 4th and 5th fingers of the right hand while descending. Lift the fingers high and play each note distinctly.

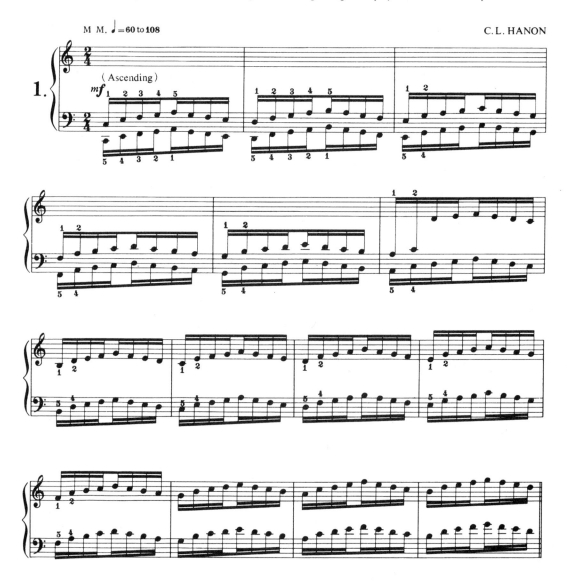

"Exercise No. 1" from THE VIRTUOSO PIANIST IN 60 EXERCISES by Hanon,
edited by Allan Small
Copyright © MCMXCII by Alfred Publishing Co., Inc.

(Descending)

As soon as Nos. 1 and 2 are mastered, go on to 2 without stopping on this note.

Selections from the

Yamaha MusicSoft Library

Printed scores from Alfred Publishing

Minuet

from *Notebook for Wolfgang*

LEOPOLD MOZART
(1719–1787)

"Minuet" from ESSENTIAL KEYBOARD REPERTOIRE, Book 1,
selected and edited by Lynn Freeman Olson
Copyright © MCMXCIII by Alfred Publishing Co., Inc.

German Dance

FRANZ JOSEPH HAYDN

"German Dance" from ESSENTIAL KEYBOARD REPERTOIRE, Book 1,
selected and edited by Lynn Freeman Olson
Copyright © MCMXCIII by Alfred Publishing Co., Inc.

Écossaise

LUDWIG van BEETHOVEN

"Écossaise" from ESSENTIAL KEYBOARD REPERTOIRE, Book 1,
selected and edited by Lynn Freeman Olson
Copyright © MCMXCIII by Alfred Publishing Co., Inc.

Minuet and Trio

Allegretto

WOLFGANG AMADEUS MOZART, K. 1

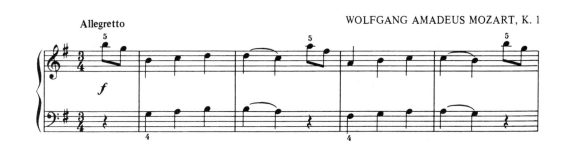

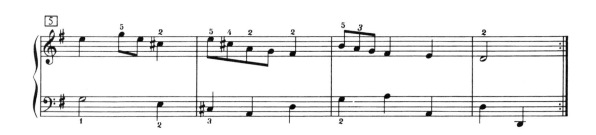

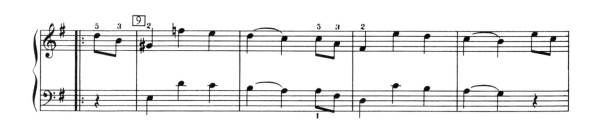

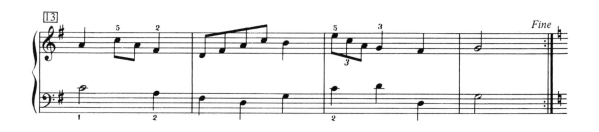

"Minuet and Trio" from ESSENTIAL KEYBOARD REPERTOIRE, Book 1,
selected and edited by Lynn Freeman Olson
Copyright © MCMXCIII by Alfred Publishing Co., Inc.

Selections from Yamaha • Minuet and Trio

Trio

*D.C. al Fine
senza rep.*

Arabesque

JOHANN FRIEDRICH BURGMÜLLER, Op. 100, No. 2
(1806–1874)

"Arabesque" from ESSENTIAL KEYBOARD REPERTOIRE, Book 1,
selected and edited by Lynn Freeman Olson
Copyright © MCMXCIII by Alfred Publishing Co., Inc.

Melody

from *Album for the Young*

ROBERT SCHUMANN, Op. 68, No. 1

Selections from Yamaha • Melody

MENUET

Attr. to Christian Pezold
BWV Anhang 115

"Menuet" from SELECTIONS FROM ANNA MAGDALENA'S NOTEBOOK, edited by Willard A. Palmer
Copyright © MCMXCII by Alfred Publishing Co., Inc.

POLONAISE

"Polonaise" from SELECTIONS FROM ANNA MAGDALENA'S NOTEBOOK, edited by Willard A. Palmer
Copyright © MCMXCII by Alfred Publishing Co., Inc.

The Wind Beneath My Wings

MIDI Orchestration by
John Henry Kreitler and Bill Cunliffe

Words and Music by
Jeff Silbar and Larry Henley

Slow Ballad ($\quad$ = 70)
Lead Instrument: Piano 1 (GM #001)

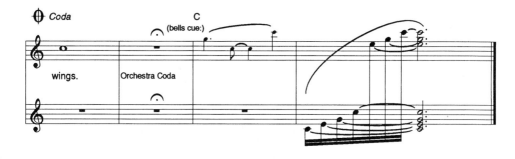

Verse 2

So I was the one with all the glory.
While you were the one with all the strength.
A beautiful face without a name for so long.
A beautiful smile to hide the pain.

Verse 3

It might have appeared to go unnoticed,
But I've got it all here in my heart.
I want you to know I know the truth.
Of course, I know it.
I would be nothing without you.

In The Midnight Hour

MIDI Orchestration by
Wes Boatman and David Rice

Words and Music by
Wilson Pickett and Steve Cropper

wait 'til the mid-night hour_____ that's when my love comes tum - blin'_____ down._____

_____ I'm gon-na wait, wait_____ 'til the mid-night hour,_____ that's when my

love be - gins to shine,_____ just you_____ and I_____

Just_____ you_____ and I_____ Just_____ you_____ and I_____

Just_____ you_____ and I_____ Just_____ you_____ and I._____

gliss.

gliss.

Verse 2
I'm gonna wait 'til the stars come out,
and see that twinkle in your eyes.
I'm gonna wait 'til the midnight hour,
that's when my love begins to shine.
You'll be the only girl I know
and really love me so, oh yeah,
in the midnight hour.

Crazy

MIDI Orchestration by
Bill Cunliffe and Randy Villars

Words and Music by
Willie Nelson

Slow Country Swing ($\quad$ = 75)

Lead Instrument: Nylon String Guitar (GM #025)

(use mod. wheel throughout for vibrato)

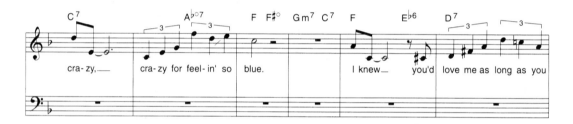

Lyrics:

Cra-zy,— cra-zy for feel-in' so lone-ly,— I'm

cra-zy,— cra-zy for feel-in' so blue. I knew— you'd love me as long as you

want-ed, And then some-day— you'd leave me for some-bo-dy new.

Wor-ry,— why do I let my-self wor-ry— Won-d'rin'—

what in the world did I do?_____ Cra-zy,___ for think-ing that my love could

hold you, I'm cra-zy for try-in', and cra-zy for cry-in', And I'm

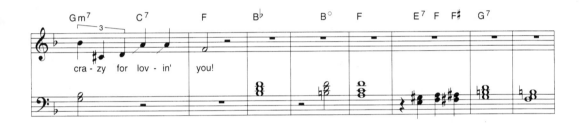

cra-zy for lov-in' you!

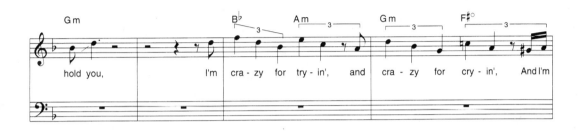

Cra-zy___ for think-ing that my love could hold you, I'm

cra-zy for try-in', and cra-zy for cry-in', And I'm cra-zy for lov-in' you!

Help Me Make It Through The Night

Words and Music by
Kris Kristofferson

Swing Feel ($\stackrel{}{}$ = 74)

Lead Instrument: Nylon Guitar (GM #025)

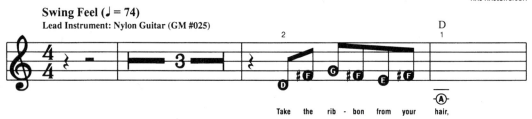

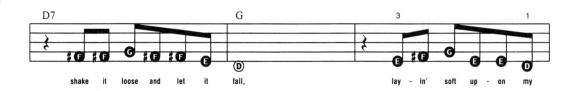

Take the rib - bon from your hair,

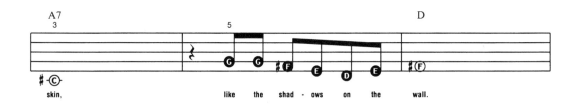

shake it loose and let it fall, lay - in' soft up - on my

skin, like the shad - ows on the wall.

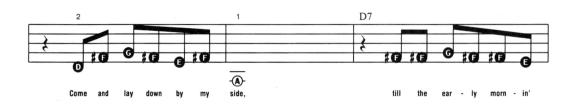

Come and lay down by my side, till the ear - ly morn - in'

light, all I'm tak - in' is your time.

Anything Goes

MIDI Orchestration by
Rick Snyder

Words and music by
Cole Porter

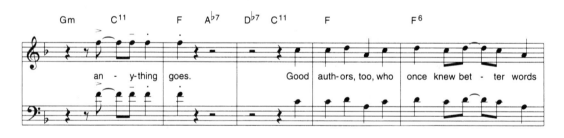

Selections from Turbo Music • Anything Goes

JLP INTERNATIONAL

"Excellence in Christian music and multimedia."

Contact us today...

- ➤ Web Site Address: http://www.jlpi.com
- ➤ Email Address: inquiry@jlpi.com
- ➤ Telephone: 508-877-8778
- ➤ FAX: 508-877-7565
- ➤ Mailing Address: JLPI | 630 Potter Road | Framingham, MA 01701

ORDER THESE EXCITING *CAKEWALK IN CONCERT* PRODUCTS:

Wedding Music
Best-Loved Hymns
Contemporary Stylings
Christian Classical Music Favorites
plus a wide range of other inspiring Christian media products!

*"Performances are of high caliber,
the keyboard and guitar music sound great. It's money well spent."*
PC MAGAZINE

Hallelujah Chorus

Revelation 19:6, 11:15, & 19:16

George Frederick Handel

O Come O Come Emmanuel

Latin Hymn, 12th Century

Music by Thomas Helmore, 1854
Arr. by Peter Vantine & JLP International, Inc.

REFRAIN

Praise To The Lord

Joachim Neander, 1680

Erneuerten Gesangbuch, Stralsund, 1665
Arr. by JLP International, Inc.

© 1998 JLP International, Inc.

Selections from JLP • Praise to the Lord

How to Get More Music

The Cakewalk In Concert Song Book includes dozens of selections from some of the best arrangements available. If you want more great MIDI and music score titles, check with your local music store for editions with MIDI arrangements. Or, simply telephone the following companies for fast delivery:

Music Dispatch	**800-637-2852**
	Your complete source for great music from **Hal Leonard, Yamaha,** and many other publishers, including other titles in the *You're the Star* series from **Turbo Music**.
Alfred Publishing	**818-892-2452**
	Alfred provides acclaimed music titles in many styles for children and adults of all abilities.
JLP International	**508-877-8778**
	Wonderful arrangements of Christian music for worship and celebration, in many musical styles, from the people who brought you the Romeo Music Library.